Enid Blyton's

CHRISTMAS TALES

A Templar Book

Produced by The Templar Company plc,
Pippbrook Mill, London Road, Dorking, Surrey RH4 1JE, Great Britain.

This edition copyright © 1992 by Darrell Waters Limited
This edition illustration and design copyright © 1992 by The Templar Company plc
Enid Blyton is a registered trademark of Darrell Waters Limited

This edition produced in the UK for Bookmart Ltd.

This book contains material first published as
The Toys Come to Life by The Brockhampton Book Co Ltd 1943,
Teddy Bear's Party by The Brockhampton Press Ltd 1945, and
Oh! What a Lovely Time by The Brockhampton Press Ltd 1949.

Illustrated by Shirley Willis and Sue Deakin

Printed and bound in Singapore

ISBN 1- 870956-90-7

Enid Blyton's
CHRISTMAS TALES

Templar

CONTENTS

The Night the Toys Came to Life

The nursery was very, very quiet. Sarah and Jack had gone to bed. All their toys were shut up safely in the big toy cupboard. It was dark in the nursery, and nothing could be heard but the ticking of the cuckoo-clock on the wall.

The cuckoo-bird suddenly popped out of the clock, flapped her wooden wings, and cried "Cuckoo!" twelve times. It was twelve o'clock, the middle of the night.

Now, one toy had been left out of the toy cupboard, just one. It was Teddy, the big brown teddy bear. He had one glass eye, and one boot-button eye. Once he had lost a glass eye, so Sarah had sewn on a button instead, and he said he could see quite well with it. Right now, Teddy was asleep, but the cuckoo woke him up with a jump.

"Who is playing hide-and-seek?" cried Teddy.

The cuckoo laughed and popped her head out of the clock-door again.

"No one," she said. "I was cuckooing twelve o'clock, that's all. Teddy, you have been left out of the cupboard! Put the light on and let all the other toys out, and have a party!"

"Oooh yes!" said Teddy. So up he got, climbed on to a chair and switched on the light. Then he ran across to the toy cupboard. He turned the key – click – and the cupboard door opened!

"Come out, toys, come out!" cried Teddy.

All the toys woke up with a jump. "Who is that calling us?" they cried. "Oh, it's you, Teddy. Can we really come out of the toy cupboard? Oh, what fun!"

Then out came the curly-haired doll, very grand in a pink silk frock. Behind came the small teddy bear with his red hat and red jumper. Then came the jack-in-the-box, the little clockwork mouse, and the clockwork clown, tumbling head-over-heels. Two toy motor-cars came next, and then all the skittles, hopping on tiny legs. The skittle-ball went with them, but he behaved well, and didn't knock the skittles down.

The pink cat and blue dog came together. They were great friends. The clockwork train puffed out, and ran all round the nursery in excitement. And Rag Doll floated down from the top of the cupboard, hanging on to her parasol, so she wouldn't land on the floor with a big bump.

"Hurry, hurry!" said Teddy. "Don't take all night walking out! We want to have some fun, and there won't be very much time."

"What shall we do?" said the curly-haired doll. "Let's do something really exciting! Shall we have a party?"

"Oh, yes, yes!" cried all the toys, and Teddy gave such a shout of delight that he quite frightened the clockwork mouse.

"I'll make some cakes on the toy stove!" said Teddy. "I'm good at that." And he set to work.

"Pink Cat and I will go to the toy sweet-shop," said the blue dog. "There are lots of sweets there. We will take some out of the bottles, and put them on little dishes. Everyone will like those."

"There is a jug of milk on the table," said the rag doll. "I will get it, and we will fill the toy tea-pot with milk, and pretend it is tea."

Rag Doll and Teddy got the jug safely down on the floor. The pink cat popped her head into the jug and took a lick. "Very nice and creamy," she said. "Oh, Teddy, how delicious your cakes smell! Open the oven door and see if they are nearly ready."

The teddy opened the little oven door, and took out the pan of cakes. They were lovely – warm and brown, smelling most delicious. "They are just ready," called Teddy.

"We had better dress ourselves up for the party," said Jack-in-the-Box. "I shall put on a new hat and polish up my brass buttons a bit."

Everyone hurried to make themselves nice for the party. The curly-haired doll brushed her hair out till it was like a cloud round her face.

She tied it up
with a blue ribbon.
The pink cat got the blue
dog to tie a fine bow round
her neck, and she tied a blue
bow round the blue dog's tail.
He looked very smart.

Even the clockwork
mouse got Small Bear to
tie a sash round his fat little
middle. "We want bows, too,"
said the skittles, but there
was no more ribbon left.
"You look quite smart in
your red uniform," said the
clockwork mouse.

"Let's ask the dolls' house dolls as well!" said Teddy.
"I am sure they would like to come!" So he knocked at the
front door of the dolls' house, and the little Mother-
doll opened it. She was so pleased when she knew there
was to be a party. "I and Daddy-doll, and all the little
children-dolls would love to come!" she said.

So they all ran out of the dolls' house in their best
frocks and suits, looking as sweet as could be.

"Now we will begin the party," said Teddy. "What shall
we sit on? There are only two dolls' chairs."

"We can each sit on a brick!" said the blue dog. "I will

get them out of the brick-box." The pink cat helped him to bring out the big wooden bricks, and they set them all round the little table. The curly-haired doll had already put a pretty cloth on it, and had arranged all the cups and saucers and plates from the toy tea-set. She had filled the big tea-pot with milk.

"I want to pour out, I want to pour out!" said the clockwork mouse. But the doll wouldn't let him. "You would spill the tea," she said. "Go and sit down like a good mouse."

Even the big rocking-horse rocked up to join the party. He chewed up four of Teddy's cakes in no time and he drank fourteen cups of tea – though really it was milk, of course.

"Your cakes are delicious, Teddy!" said the rag doll, and the bear blushed bright red with pride. He looked quite funny for a minute, but he soon became his usual colour again. It really was a lovely party.

"Has everyone had enough to eat?" asked Teddy at last. "There isn't anything left – not even a sweet, and the tea-pot is empty. What shall we do now?"

"Play games and dance!" cried the blue dog. "Let's play catch! I'll catch you, Small Bear, I'll catch you!" The small teddy bear gave a squeal and ran away. The clockwork clown went head-over-heels as fast as ever he could, and upset all the skittles.

Bang-smack-bang! Down they went with such a noise. The clockwork mouse squealed loudly when one skittle fell on top of him.

"I feel like singing," said the pink cat suddenly. "I want to sing." So she opened her mouth and sang loudly, but nobody liked her song at all. "It's nothing but 'Meow, meow, meow'!" said the curly-haired doll. "Do stop, Pink Cat."

"I want to dance!" cried a big skittle. "We skittles can dance beautifully. We want some music."

"Well, start the musical box then," said Teddy.
"I'll wind the handle. Are you ready?" And then
the nursery was suddenly full of loud tinkling music
as the teddy turned the handle of the musical box.
What a noise there was!

Now, outside in the street, the night watchman was doing his round, with his torch in his hand. He was shining it on to people's front-doors to make sure they were fast-shut. He was a very good night watchman indeed.

Suddenly he came to a stop. "I hear a strange noise!" he said. "What can it be? It is music playing! It is people squealing and laughing. It is somebody singing a loud Meow song. What a very strange thing to hear in the middle of the night!"

He listened for a little while, and then he made up his mind to find out what all the noise was about. "I am sure the people of the house are all in bed!" he said. "Ho! Who can it be making all this dreadful noise? I must certainly stop it."

Now the toys hadn't heard the night watchman walking by outside, because they were making such a noise. Suddenly they heard a knocking at the window! "Oooh, what's that?" cried Teddy in a fright. "Turn out the light, quickly!"

So the curly-haired doll switched off the light – and then, in at the window shone the night watchman's torch. Oh, what a fright the toys got! "Save me, save me!" cried the clockwork mouse and bumped into all the skittles and knocked them down, clitter-clatter, clitter-clatter.

"What's going on here?" said the deep voice of the night watchman, and he climbed in at the window. He shone his light all round the nursery. "What, nobody here but toys?" he said in great surprise. "Then what could that noise have been?"

"Please, it was us," said the teddy, in a very small voice. The night watchman was so astonished when he heard the teddy speaking to him that he couldn't say a word.

"You see, we were having a party," said the curly-haired doll, and she switched on the light again. Then the night watchman saw the remains of the party on the table. "Teddy baked some cakes, and the pink cat got some sweets from the toy sweet-shop," said the doll.

"Oh, what a pity I didn't come a bit sooner," said the big night watchman. "I could have had a cake then. I get so hungry in the middle of the night."

"I'll make you some!" cried Teddy, hurrying to the toy stove. "Have a ride on the rocking-horse whilst the cakes are baking. They won't take long!"

So the night watchman got on to the rocking-horse, and the horse gave him a fine ride whilst the cakes were cooking.

The teddy bear baked a beautiful
batch of cakes. The pink cat filled a little
dish with more sweets from the shop. The
curly-haired doll tipped up the big jug and filled
the tea-pot once more. The dolls' house mother-doll
took a cup and saucer and plate into the dolls' house
and washed it for the night watchman.

Suddenly something happened! The kitchen cat came
creeping in at the door, for she had heard all the noise too.
She stood there looking at the busy toys – and she
suddenly saw the clockwork mouse rushing across the floor!

"A mouse, a mouse!" she mewed, and she pounced on
the frightened mouse at once. The mouse's key flew out
of his side, and he gave a loud squeal. "Let the mouse
go!" cried Teddy. "Bad cat!" shouted the clockwork clown.

But the cat would not let the poor little mouse go. Then the big night watchman got off the rocking-horse and walked over to the cat. He took out his black notebook and a big pencil.

"I must have your name and address," he said to the surprised cat. "I must report you for cruelty to animals. See how you have frightened this poor little mouse!"

The cat fled away in fright. The toys crowded round the night watchman. "Oh, thank you, thank you, kind Night Watchman!" they cried.

"You are so kind," said the clockwork mouse, rubbing his little nose against the night watchman's boots. "I wish you were my very own Night Watchman. I do like you!"

S.W.

"Come and eat my cakes," said Teddy. The night watchman looked at them. "Dear me!" he said. "I shall never be able to eat all those! Can't we ask someone else to come and share them with me?"

"Let's ask Sarah and Jack!" cried Teddy. "They are asleep, but we can soon wake them."

"You go," said the rag doll. "Tell them we want them to share in our fun. They are nice children and have always been kind to us. It would be fun to share the party with them."

So the teddy went out of the door and tiptoed to the children's room. He climbed up on to the bed and pulled at the sheet. "Wake up," he said, "wake up. There's a party going on!"

Sarah and Jack woke up. They *were* surprised to see Teddy. "Have you come alive?" they said. "Of course I have," said Teddy. "Do hurry up and come to the party!"

So the two children put on their dressing-gowns and slippers, and went to share the toys' party. They couldn't help feeling very excited.

"Here they come, here they come!" said the toys to one another. "Hello, Sarah; hello, Jack!"

The two children walked into the nursery and were most surprised to see all the toys running about, and the skittles hopping, and the two motor-cars rushing over the carpet.

But they were even more surprised to see the big night watchman. "Good gracious!" said Sarah, staring at him. "What are you doing in our nursery in the middle of the night?"

The night watchman told them. "I heard such a noise in here, and I came to see what the matter was," he said. "Then the toys kindly invited me to their party. But the teddy bear made so many cakes that I knew I couldn't eat them all myself. So he went to fetch you two."

"Oh, how lovely!" said Sarah. "Teddy, I didn't know you could make cakes. You never said a word about it!"

Teddy bowed low and went very red again. He couldn't help feeling very proud. "Please sit down on the floor," he said, "and I and the dolls will wait on you. It is a great honour to have you and the big night watchman at our party!"

So the two children and the night watchman sat down on the floor, and all the toys waited on them. "Will you have a cup of tea?" asked the curly-haired doll, handing a full cup and saucer to Sarah. "It's really only milk," she said in a whisper.

"It tastes *just* like tea," said Sarah, and she drank out of the tiny cup.

"Will you have one of my cakes?" said Teddy, and offered a plate of his little brown cakes. The children thought they were simply delicious. They crunched them up at once and told the teddy bear that they had never tasted such lovely cakes before. This time Teddy went purple with pride, and the clockwork mouse stared at him in surprise. "Did you know you were purple?" he asked. "You do look funny, Teddy."

The night watchman ate a big meal too – in fact he ate twenty-three of Teddy's cakes, and a whole dish of sweets. He drank sixteen cups of tea, which was even more than the rocking-horse had had.

It was a lovely meal, except when the rocking-horse came too near and nibbled some of the night watchman's hair off. That made him rather cross and he took out his notebook again. The rocking-horse was afraid of being asked to give his name and address so he moved away quickly.

"Now what shall we do?" asked Sarah, when they had eaten all the cakes and sweets. "We can't very well play games with you toys, because we are rather too big, and we should make such a noise."

"We will give a fine show for you!" said Small Bear. "We will set the musical box going, and the curly-haired doll shall dance her best dance. She really does dance beautifully!"

So the curly-haired doll danced her best dance to the
music, and everyone clapped their hands. Then the
clockwork clown showed how well he could knock down
all the skittles by going head-over-heels, but the skittles
were tired of that and they chased the clown all round the
nursery. He got into the brick-box and the skittles locked
him in there for quite ten minutes. That did make the
children laugh.

Then the two motor-cars ran a race with the clockwork train and that was great fun. They all bumped into one another and fell over at the end, so nobody knew who won. Then Small Bear stood on his head and waved his feet in the air. Everybody thought he was very clever. "Can you do that, Night Watchman?" asked Teddy.

"I don't know. I'll try," said the big night watchman, and he got up. But he couldn't do tricks like Small Bear.

He soon sat down again, and mopped his head with a big red handkerchief. "I'd rather watch you do tricks than try them myself," he said. "Hallo – what's this?"

The night watchman and the children saw that the toy farm had suddenly come to life. It stood in a corner of the nursery, and nobody had thought of waking up the farmer, his wife, and animals. But they had heard the noise of the party, and now they were all very lively indeed!

"The ducks are swimming on the pond!" said Sarah.

"The cows are nibbling the toy grass," said Jack.

"The hens are laying little eggs!" said the night watchman in surprise. "And look at those tiny lambs frisking about! There goes the farmer to milk his cows. Well, well, well – it's a wonderful sight to see!"

The toy farm-dog barked round the sheep. The toy horse dragged the toy farm-cart along. The toy pigs grunted and rooted about in their little toy sty. The children really loved watching everything.

"Oh!" said Sarah. "I have always, always wanted our toy farm to come alive – and now it has. Jack, isn't it lovely? Oh, do look – the farmer's wife is offering us a tiny, tiny egg!" So she was. The night watchman and the two children took one each. They were very pleased.

Just as they were all watching the toy farm, a loud noise made everyone jump. It was the toy cockerel on the farm, crowing as loudly as ever he could.

"Cock-a-doodle-doo! Cock-a-doodle-doo!"

"It's day-break!" cried Teddy, in surprise. "How quickly the time has gone."

"It's dawn!" cried the curly-haired doll. "The sun will soon be up. Time for all toys to go back to the cupboard. Hurry now, hurry!

"We must not be alive after day-break. Hurry, toys!"

Then what a hurry-scurry there was for the toy
cupboard! The night watchman and the children watched
in surprise. The skittles hopped in. The clockwork mouse
tore in at top speed. The clockwork clown went
head-over-heels right into the back of the cupboard. The
pink cat and blue dog ran together, their whiskers
touching. Teddy put the bricks into the box
quickly. The dolls' house dolls cleared
away the tea-things, and then
ran to their house and
shut the front door.

"Good-night – or rather, good-morning!" said Teddy, popping his head out of the cupboard. "So glad you came and shared our fun! Good-bye – and come again another day!"

"Well, that's all over," said Sarah, with a sigh. "Oh, wasn't it fun? Did you enjoy it too, Night Watchman?"

"I should think I did," said the night watchman. "Well, I must be getting back to my work, or somebody will be after me. And you two had better go to bed. I'll get out of the window. Good-night!"

"Good-night!" said Sarah and Jack. They watched the night watchman get out of the window and then they went to the nursery door. "Good-night, toys," they said softly.

And out of the toy cupboard came a crowd of tiny voices, from the little growl of Small Bear to the squeak of the clockwork mouse. "Good-night, Sarah and Jack, good-night!"

Then Teddy poked his head out of the cupboard again. "It was all because you didn't put me away in the cupboard tonight that the party happened!" he said. "Leave me out again sometime, please!"

"We will!" said the children. What fun they'll have when they do!

Brown Bear has a Birthday

Once there was a brown teddy bear called Ben.
For a long time he lived on a shelf in a toy-shop.

Then one day a little girl bought him. She took him home and showed him to all the toys in her nursery.

"Look!" she said. "Here is a new friend for you, toys – a bear called Ben. Isn't he lovely! He's soft to cuddle – and just listen to the noise he makes when I press his middle."

"Ooooomph!" said Ben the Brown Bear, when Sarah pressed him hard in the middle. He felt very proud when Sarah spoke of him like that.

Sarah loved her new bear. She took him to bed with her at night, and the rag doll didn't like that, because she had always been the one to go to bed with Sarah.

Ben was proud of his growl. But the toys got very tired of it. "Ooooomph! Ooooomph! Ooooomph!" They heard the noise all night long when they got up to play.

"Stop making that noise," said the rag doll. "I'm tired of it. Go and creep back into Sarah's bed. You oughtn't to leave her if she takes you to bed at night."

"I like playing with all of you," said Ben, and he pressed his middle again. "Ooooomph! I don't leave Sarah until she's asleep, and I always creep back before the morning. Ooooomph!"

Sarah gave Ben a blue ribbon to tie round his neck. He was very pleased. He stood in front of a mirror and looked at himself.

"I am a very good-looking bear, aren't I?" he said to the pink cat. She had been cleaning her fur, and she thought the bear was silly and vain. Everyone knew that the pink cat was the prettiest of all the toys. Ben thought too much of himself!

"I don't think you're at all good-looking," said the pink cat. "Your nose is too stubby, you're too fat, and I am tired of your ooooomphing."

"You're horrible," said the bear, and turned his back on the cat.

He walked away and trod on the tail of the clockwork mouse.

"Oh – you've hurt my tail!" said the little mouse. "Say you're sorry."

"Shan't!" said Ben, and he didn't.

"You haven't any manners,"
said the clockwork mouse.
"I shall go and tell the rag doll about you."
"Tell-tale!" said Ben, and he trod on the mouse's tail
again. The mouse squealed and tried to run over to the rag
doll to tell her about Ben. But he couldn't because Ben
wouldn't get off his tail.

Nobody felt very pleased with the bear after that.
They wouldn't play catch or hide-and-seek with him. They
wouldn't help him to untie his blue ribbon when it got into
a knot.

Ben felt very sad. He went to the oldest toy in the nursery, the wise old rocking-horse, whose long tail had once been chewed by Sarah's dog. It looked very sad. But Rocking-horse was very clever, and toys always went to him when they were in trouble.

"Rocking-horse, the toys are horrid to me," said Ben. "It makes me sad."

"Perhaps you've been nasty to them?" said Rocking-horse, swinging his chewed tail.

"I'm not – not really, anyway," said Ben. "I'd like to be nice to them, really I would. But they tell me I am horrid, and they won't let me play with them."

"Well, you be very, very nice to them and see what happens," said Rocking-horse. "Now, listen to me – you've got a birthday coming soon, haven't you?"

"Yes," said Ben. "So I have. I'd quite forgotten it!"

"Well, now, you give a lovely party to the toys," said Rocking-horse. "Give them a lovely meal, and plan lots of

games, and you'll soon see they will forget you were ever nasty.''

"That's a very good idea,'' said Ben. "I *will* give a party! I'll think about it hard.'' So he did. But he wasn't used to giving parties, and he wondered how to do it.

"I must look in my money-box and see if I have any money there,'' he said to himself. "If I have, I can buy some cakes and sweets and lemonade.''

But there wasn't anything in his money-box at all, which wasn't surprising, because Ben had never put anything into it. He was sad.

"Now what shall I do?" he thought. "I really must have a party. I know! I will creep into the toy sweet-shop when nobody is looking, and take some little bags of sweets. They will do nicely for the party." Now this was very naughty of him, because they were not his sweets to take. But he didn't think of that. He only thought of his party.

One night, when the toys had all gone into the toy-cupboard to have a rest after a game of hide-and-seek, Ben crept over to the toy sweet-shop. It was a lovely place. There were tiny bottles of sweets, very small bars of chocolate, some little scales for weighing, and lots of paper bags to put the sweets in.

"I'll take a bag of boiled sweets," thought Ben, and he emptied some sweets out of one of the bottles into a bag. Then he took down another bottle. It was full of tiny round chocolates. Ben tasted one to see if it was good.

Then he got a dreadful shock! Someone popped up from behind the little counter and caught him by the shoulder!

"You bad bear! You're stealing my sweets!" cried an angry voice.

Ben saw that the little sweet-shop doll was glaring at him, looking very cross.

"I wasn't stealing them! They were for my party! Everyone was going to have some," said Ben.

But the sweet-shop doll wouldn't believe him. He called to the other toys. "Come and see this bad bear. I caught him stealing sweets, and eating them, too! And all he says is that he was taking them for a party!"

"Party? What party? *We've* not heard of any party!" cried the toys.

Ben threw down the bags of
sweets and went away with tears
in his little button eyes.
Nobody believed him.
They thought he was a bad bear.
What a pity! If only he could
have a lovely party and make
everyone happy,
the toys would be
nice to him again.

"I wonder if there are any cakes in the dolls' kitchen," he thought, later on. "I am sure I smelt something cooking earlier. I expect the dolls had a baking day, and baked some cakes in their little stove. I might ask them for some and put them away for my party."

So he went over to ask them. But when he arrived, the kitchen was empty. The dolls were all out paying a visit to the skittles. Ben pushed open the door and went in. He called out softly.

"Is anybody here?" But nobody answered, because there was nobody there.

Ben went into the little kitchen. It was a lovely kitchen. The shelves were full of shiny pots and pans.

He opened the cupboard at the back of the kitchen – and there he saw a whole plate of tiny cakes, freshly baked!

"Good!" said Ben. "I will have these for my party.

I will tell the dolls when I see them. I am sure
they will let me have them for my party.''
    He was just leaving with the plate full of
cakes when three of the dolls came back from
visiting the skittles.

When they saw Ben coming out with their plate of cakes they were very, very cross indeed.

"Look at this naughty teddy bear!" they cried. "First he tried to take the sweets and now he takes our cakes!" And they told him off very severely and wouldn't listen to a word he said. None of the toys would speak to him after that, and he was very unhappy.

"I tried to do my best to have a party, but it's no good, the toys are even more unfriendly than ever!" he told the rocking-horse. "I shall run away."

"No, don't do that," said the rocking-horse. "It is a great mistake to run away from things. You set about having your party in the wrong way, you know. You should have asked the others to help you."

"I won't ask a single one of them to help me, ever!" said the bear, and he looked so angry that the rocking-horse knew it was no good talking to him any more.

The other toys came to the rocking-horse, too, and told him about the bear.

"We can't think why he is so unfriendly," they said. "He looks quite a friendly bear. But he behaves so badly."

"He's a very young bear," said Rocking-horse. "He does things the wrong way. He wanted to be nice to you, really. What about being nice to him?"

"Oh, no. He doesn't deserve it," said Rag Doll.

"But it would be worth it if it makes him nice and friendly again," said Rocking-horse. "It is bad to make yourselves into enemies when you could be friends."

"Well – how could we be nice to him?" said the pink cat.

"It's his birthday next week," said Rocking-horse. "What about giving him a party? He would love that, and so would you."

Now, somehow, that seemed a very good idea to the toys. They loved a party and, after all, if it was Ben the Brown Bear's birthday, he ought to have a party.

"We'll give him one,' said the rag doll. "Yes, we really will!" So all the toys began to plan a fine party. But they thought they wouldn't tell the bear. It was to be a birthday surprise for him.

They went into corners and talked about it. They were always whispering together. Ben couldn't think what their secret was.

"They are saying horrible things about me!" he thought. "I shall run away. Yes, I really shall, I won't stay in this nasty nursery."

But the toys were only planning his party. The sweet-shop doll said he would give twelve of each of his little sweets and chocolates for the party.

"Oh, good!" said the pink cat. "That will be lovely. We all like your sweets."

"And we will bake some cakes," said the dolls.

"We will make a big birthday cake, too, with two candles on. And we will make some jam-tarts. You all like those."

"I'll make some lemonade," said the rag doll.

"Hurray!" said the clockwork mouse, "that's my favourite."

"We won't make the cakes or jam-tarts till the day of the birthday," said the dolls. "They will be nice and fresh then."

"We'd better give the bear some presents," said the clockwork mouse. "I could give him that blue button I found on the floor the other day."

"And I could give him my red ball," said the pink cat. "I like it very much; so I expect Ben would like it, too."

"Oh, he would," said the rag doll. "It would be a lovely present. I think I'll make him some striped trousers from that material I've been saving for something special."

"Ben would look lovely in trousers," said the curly-haired doll. "I shall give him a bright sash to go round his waist, to keep his trousers up."

Clockwork Clown couldn't think
of anything at all to give him.
"I know," he said. "I'll paint him
a most beautiful birthday card,"
he said. "He must have a
birthday card. Everybody
does on a birthday."

Now, with all these exciting secrets going on, Ben grew more and more puzzled and sad.

Why wouldn't anyone tell him the secrets? Even Rocking-horse said nothing about them. Ben went into a corner and thought hard.

"Perhaps I am a horrid little bear," he said to himself. "I expect I am vain. And I shouldn't have gone about pressing my middle and growling all the time. I won't ooooomph any more. And – oh, dear – I shouldn't have taken the sweets and cakes without asking!"

The more he thought about things, the worse he felt. At last he made up his mind that he was so horrid he really should go away.

He felt sure nobody in the nursery would like him any more.

"I'll creep away on my birthday," he thought. "I won't tell anyone I am going. I'll put on my hat and go."

Well, when his birthday came, there was great excitement in the nursery, because all the toys were getting ready for the party!

Little tables and chairs were set out everywhere, and cups and plates and dishes were put on them.

A delicious smell came from the dolls' kitchen, because lots of cakes and jam-tarts had been made – and a most beautiful birthday cake with two candles on it!

The lemonade was in a big jug. Little dishes of sweets were on the table. The toys were dressing up in fancy dress and getting more and more excited.

"They're having a party, and they didn't tell me anything about it," thought the bear sadly, and he went and fetched his hat. "I shall go now, whilst they are getting ready for it."

Now, just as he was walking out of the door the clockwork clown called to him.

"Hey, Ben! Where are you going?" he said.

"I'm running away. I'm a horrid little bear, and nobody here will ever like me," said Ben. "But I'm sorry I was horrid. Good-bye, Clockwork Clown."

"Wait! Wait!" cried Clockwork Clown, and he ran over to Ben with the birthday card he had painted for him. "Many happy returns of the day, Ben! Here's a birthday card for you!"

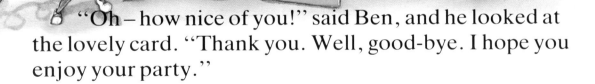

"Oh – how nice of you!" said Ben, and he looked at the lovely card. "Thank you. Well, good-bye. I hope you enjoy your party."

The other toys came running up, all looking very smart. "Ben! It's *your* party, silly! It's for you. Many happy returns of the day, and do please come to your own birthday party!"

Well! Ben could hardly believe his ears. His very own birthday party!

"I don't understand," he said. "How can it be mine?"

"It was a secret! We planned it for you!" said the pink cat. "Here's my present for you – a red ball to play with."

"Oh, thank you! How lovely!" said the bear. He began to feel tremendously happy. "I do wish I'd got some party clothes on, too. You all look so nice."

"Well, put some on," said the rag doll, and gave him the new striped trousers. "These are for you."

"And you can tie this round your waist," said the curly-haired doll, and gave him the lovely sash.

Ben put on the striped trousers and the sash. They did look fine!

The clockwork mouse gave him the blue button he had found, and the curly-haired doll sewed it on the front of his trousers. Ben looked at himself in the mirror. He thought he looked very fine indeed – but he didn't say so! He let the others say it for him!

"You look fine, Ben! You look wonderful!" they cried. "The trousers fit you well."

"And now let's have the party," said Rocking-horse as the dolls came out carrying plates of biscuits and tarts – and a big plate with the birthday cake on!

"Many happy returns of the day!" they cried, and Ben felt happier than ever. How nice everyone was! How could he ever have thought they were horrid?

They sat down to the party. The biscuits were delicious. The jam-tarts were lovely. The sweets were the nicest Ben had ever eaten. The lemonade was very tasty.

All the toys drank to Ben's health. Then they cut the
birthday cake. Ben had to cut the first slice, because it was
his birthday. After that the clockwork clown helped him,
because there were so many slices to cut.

"Wish when you take the first bite!" cried the curly-haired doll. "You always have to do that with birthday cakes!"

So everyone wished.

Then the toys cleared away the tea things, the chairs and tables were set aside, and the party games began. They played hide-and-seek and hunt-the-thimble, and then a lively game of musical chairs.

Everyone was happy and sleepy when the party was over. They climbed into the toy-cupboard to go to sleep – all except Ben, who crept, as usual, into Sarah's bed!

"Where have you been, Ben?" said Sarah, waking up.

"Ooooomph!" said Ben, sleepily. "To my birthday party. I've had a lovely time. And I do think the toys are the very nicest in all the world. I shall never, never run away from them!"

"Your *birthday party!*" said Sarah. "I must be asleep and dreaming!" But she knew she hadn't been asleep when, next morning, she saw Ben the Brown Bear still dressed in his party clothes! It was quite true, wasn't it? He *had* been to his party – and what a lovely one it was!

Christmas in the Toyshop

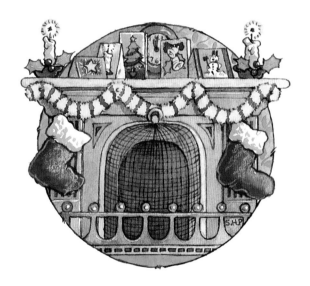

Once upon a time there was a toy-shop. It sold sweets as well as toys, so it was a very nice shop indeed.

All the children loved it. They used to come each day and press their noses against the window, and look in to see what toys there were.

"Oh look at that beautiful doll!" they would say. "Oh, do you see that train with its three carriages – and it's got lines to run on too."

"Look at the rocking-horse. I do love his friendly face!"

"Oh, what a lovely shop this is! When we grow up let's keep a shop *just* like this one!"

Miss Roundy, the shopkeeper, liked having a toy-shop. She liked seeing the children and showing them all her toys, and she nearly always gave them an extra sweet or two in their bags when they came to spend their pocket money. So, of course, the children all loved her.

The toys loved her, too.

"Look – she found me a new key when mine dropped behind the shelf and couldn't be found," said the clockwork train.

"And she put a spot of red paint on my coat where some got rubbed off," said one of the toy soldiers. "She's very, very kind."

The toys liked living in Miss Roundy's shop till they were bought by the children. It was fun to sit on the shelves and the counter, and watch the boys and girls come in and hear them talk. And it was very exciting when one of them was bought, and taken proudly away by a child.

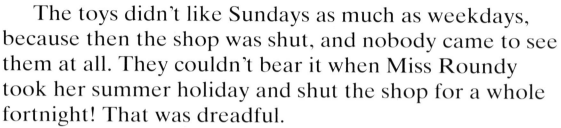

The toys didn't like Sundays as much as weekdays, because then the shop was shut, and nobody came to see them at all. They couldn't bear it when Miss Roundy took her summer holiday and shut the shop for a whole fortnight! That was dreadful.

"It's so *dull*," complained the biggest teddy bear, and he pressed his middle to make himself growl mournfully. "There's no one to see and nothing to do. Miss Roundy even pulls down the window-blind so that we can't see the children looking in at us."

And then Christmas time came, and the toys had a shock. Miss Roundy was going to close the shop for four whole days and go away to stay with her aunt. Oh dear!

"Four days of dullness and quietness and darkness," said the rocking-horse, gloomily. "Nothing to do. No one to come and buy us, or see how nice we are. Four whole days!"

A black monkey with a red ribbon around his neck

spoke in a high, chattering voice.

"Can't we have a Christmas party for ourselves?"

"It's an idea," said the rocking-horse, smiling. "Let's all think about it till Christmas comes – then we'll have a GRAND time in here by ourselves!"

The day came when Miss Roundy was going to shut the shop. She pulled down the big window-blind. Then she turned to the watching toys.

"I'm going now, toys," she said. "I shan't see you again for four whole days. Be good. A happy Christmas to you – and try and have a good time yourselves. Do what you like – *I* shan't mind! Happy Christmas!"

She went out of the shop and locked the door. The toys heard her foot-steps going down the street.

"Happy Christmas, Miss Roundy!" said everyone, softly. "You're nice!"

And now they were all alone for four days. *What* were they going to do?

The toys did what they always did as soon as the shop was shut for the night. They got up and stretched themselves, because they got stiff with sitting so long on the shelves and counter.

"That's better," said the rag doll, shaking out her legs one after another to loosen them.

The pink cat rolled over and over. "Ah – that was good," she said, standing up again. "I do love a roll."

The little clockwork train whistled loudly and the toy soldiers climbed out of their boxes and began marching to and fro.

"Nice to stretch our legs a bit," they said, and then they scattered because the roly-poly man came rolling along, not looking where he was going, as usual.

"Look out," cried the captain of the soldiers, "you'll bump into the dolls' house! There he goes, rolling to and fro – what a way to get about!"

"Listen, everyone!" called the rocking-horse. "Let's talk about Christmas."

"When is it?" asked the big teddy bear.

"The day after tomorrow," said the rocking-horse. "I think if we're going to have a good Christmas ourselves we ought to make our plans now, and get everything going, so that we're ready by Christmas Day."

"Oh yes!" cried everyone, and they all came round the rocking-horse. What a crowd there was. All the little dolls' house dolls, and the other bigger dolls, the skittles, the railway train with its carriages, and another wooden train, and the roly-poly man, and … well, I couldn't possibly tell you them all, but you know what toys there are in a toy-shop, don't you?

"Sit down," said the rocking-horse. And everyone sat, except, of course, the things that could only stand, like the trains and the motor cars and the balls.

"We shall want a party," said the rocking-horse. "That means we must have things to eat. We can take any of the sweets and chocolates we like, to make into cakes and things – Miss Roundy said we were to help ourselves."

"We can make the food," said the dolls' house dolls.

"We'll help," said the skittles, excitedly.

"We can cook on that nice toy stove over there," said the twin dolls. One of the twins was a boy doll and the other was a girl doll, and they were exactly alike.

"The pink cat and the black monkey can arrange a circus," said the rocking-horse. "They'll have great fun working together on that."

"I'll do the Christmas tree," said the clockwork sailor. "We'll have presents for everyone under it! We'll play games afterwards, too."

"What a pity Father Christmas doesn't know about us!" said the roly-poly man. "It would be so nice if he came to the party."

"I don't suppose he'll be able to come," said the black monkey. "He's much too busy at Christmas time. Don't roll against me like that, roly-poly man. You'll knock me over."

The roly-poly man rolled away and bumped into a row of soldiers. They went down on the floor at once. As they got up and brushed themselves down, they shouted angrily at the roly-poly man.

"Don't let's quarrel," said the rocking-horse. "People should never quarrel at Christmas-time. It's a time to make one another happy and glad. Now – to your work, everyone – and we'll see what a wonderful Christmas Day we will have!"

The dolls and the skittles set to work at once. The doll with golden hair and the twin dolls took charge of

the cooking. They got the little toy cooker going, and there was soon a *most* delicious smell in the toy-shop – the cakes were baking!

There were chocolate cakes and fudge cakes and peppermint buns. There were little jellies made of the jelly sweets Miss Roundy sold. There was a very big iced cake with tiny candles on it that the rag doll had found in a box.

The baking and cooking went on all day long. The twin dolls had to scold the roly-poly man ever so many times because he would keep rolling against the golden-haired doll just as she was taking cakes out of the oven.

Still, as you can see, there was plenty of everything.

"What a feast we are going to have!" said the rag doll, greedily. "Ooooh – fudge cakes – I'll have six of those, please, on Christmas Day!"

The clockwork sailor did the Christmas tree. He was very, very clever. He climbed right up to the topmost

shelf, which Miss Roundy had decorated with evergreens, and he chose a very nice bit of fir.

"Look out!" he called. "I'm going to push it off the shelf." So everyone looked out, and down came the little branch of fir tree, flopping on to the floor.

The clockwork sailor climbed down. He did a little dance of joy when he saw what a wonderful tree the bit of fir would make. He wondered what to put it in.

"If you'll get me out of my box, so that I can join in the fun for once, you can use my box," said the gruff voice of Jack-in-the-Box.

The toys didn't really like Jack-in-the-Box very much. He lived inside a square box, and when the box was opened he suddenly leapt out on a long spring, and frightened them very much. The clockwork sailor didn't really know if he wanted to get Jack out of his box.

"Go on – just this once,"
said Jack-in-the-Box.
"I promise to be good.
I'll perform in the circus,
and be funny if you like."
    So Jack-in-the-Box
was taken out of his box
and he wobbled everywhere
on his long spring, enjoying
his freedom very much.

The box was just right for the Christmas tree. The clockwork sailor filled it with earth that he took from the pot that held a big plant belonging to Miss Roundy. Then he planted the bit of fir tree in it.

"Now to decorate it!" he said. So he got some tiny coloured candles and some bright beads out of the bead box, and some tinsel from the counter, and anything else he could think of – and dear me, the tree really began to look very beautiful!

"I can make a star to go on the top of the tree," said the teddy bear, and he ran off to find some silver paper.

"And now you're none of you to look," said the sailor, "because I'm going to pack up presents for you – yes, a present for every single one of you!"

The circus was practising hard. There were two clockwork clowns in the toy-shop, so they were exactly right for the circus. They could go head-over-heels as fast as could be.

"We want some horses," said the black monkey, who was very busy. "Pink cat, stop prowling round the cakes, and see how many horses you can find."

The roly-poly man said he wanted to be a clown, so the teddy bear made him a clown's hat, and let him roll about the ring, knocking people over. Jack-out-of-his-Box jumped about and waggled his head on his long neck. He was really very funny.

The pink cat borrowed some horses from the soldiers and the farm. She led them down to the circus ring.

Noah arrived with his animals from the ark. There were elephants, lions, tigers and even kangaroos!

"It's going to be a GRAND circus!" said the pink cat. "Oh, hurry up and come, Christmas Day!"

Well, Christmas Day did come at last! The toys rushed to one another, shouting "Happy Christmas! Happy Christmas!" at the tops of their voices.

The railway train whistled its loudest. The big bear and the little bears pressed themselves in the middle and growled. The musical box began to play, and the rag doll sat down at the toy piano and played a rollicking tune.

Nobody knew she could play and they were all very surprised. So was the rag doll. She hadn't known either, and once she had begun to play she couldn't stop! So what with the engine's whistle, the bears' growling, the musical box's tunes and the piano there was a very fine noise.

The roly-poly man got so excited that he knocked over two of the horses, rolled on the monkey's tail and upset a jug of lemonade.

"Can't you stop rolling about and be still for a moment?" said the pink cat, keeping her tail well out of the way.

"I can't stand still," said the roly-poly man, "because I've got something very heavy at the bottom of me. It makes me wobble, but not fall over. I really will try to be good – but if you were as wobbly as I am you'd find it difficult, too."

The black monkey suddenly appeared dressed up in white trousers and a top hat! He carried a whip in his hand. He cracked it and made everyone jump.

Then the pink cat appeared, carrying a drum. She beat it – boom-diddy-boom-diddy-boom-boom-boom. "The circus is about to begin!" shouted the black monkey and he cracked his whip again. "Walk up, everyone! The circus is about to begin!"

"Boom-diddy-boom-diddy-boom!" went the drum.

All the toys rushed for seats. The black monkey had arranged bricks of all sizes and shapes out of the brick-boxes for seats and there was room for everyone. The dolls' house dolls were allowed to be at the front because they were so small.

The skittles were so excited that they kept giggling and falling over.

"Quiet there! Settle down please!" shouted the monkey. "Pink cat, sound the drum again – the performers are about to march in."

The circus began. You really should have seen it. The horses were splendid. They ran round the ring one way, and then turned and went the other way.

Then the clowns came on, with Jack and the roly-poly man. The roly-poly man rolled all over the place and knocked all the clowns over. Then the clowns tried to catch Jack, but they couldn't, of course, because Jack sprang about all over the place, on his long spring. The toys almost cried with laughter.

The elephants were cheered when they came in. They waved their trunks in the air and trumpeted as loudly as they could. The lions and tigers came in and roared fiercely. The kangaroos jumped all round the ring and the bears walked in standing up on their hind legs.

All the toys clapped and cheered and stamped at the end, and said it was the very best circus in the world. The pink cat and the black monkey felt very proud and they stood in the middle of the ring and bowed to everyone so many times that they really made their backs ache.

"Now for the tea party!" called the doll with golden hair. "Come along! You must be very hungry, toys – hurry up and come to the party!"

What a wonderful tea party it was! There were little tables everywhere. In the middle of them were vases of flowers that the dolls had picked out of the dolls' hats that Miss Roundy kept in a box on a special shelf.

The tables were set with the cups and saucers and plates out of the boxes of toy tea sets. There was a tea-pot on each, full of lemonade to pour into the cups.

The cakes were lovely. There were fudge cakes, peppermint buns, chocolate cakes, all kinds of biscuits, toffee sandwiches, jellies that wobbled like the roly-poly man and, of course, the Christmas cake was the best thing of all.

"We've put it on a table by itself, because it's so big," said the golden-haired doll. "I hope there'll be a slice for everybody."

It looked lovely. The golden-haired doll had decorated it with icing. Everyone thought that was very clever indeed.

The pink cat ate so much that she got fatter than ever. The captain of the soldiers lent the twin dolls his sharp sword to cut the cake. The roly-poly man rolled up to see them cutting it, and nearly got his head cut off!

When nobody could eat any more, and all the lemonade was drunk, the skittles cleared away. "We'll wash up and put all the tea sets back in their boxes," they said. "The rest of you can play games."

So, whilst the skittles were busy, the toys played party games. They played blind man's buff, and the blindfolded pink cat caught the elephant out of the Noah's Ark.

"Who can it be?" wondered the pink cat, feeling the elephant carefully. All the toys laughed, because of course, they knew who it was.

They played hunt the thimble, and nobody could see for a long time where the thimble was hidden. Then the clockwork sailor gave a scream.

"The captain of the soldiers is wearing it for a helmet – he is, he is!"

And so he was. He was sorry to give it up because he thought it was a very nice helmet indeed.

The trains gave everyone rides, and so did the toy motor cars. Even the aeroplane said it would fly round the nursery once with everybody. The musical box played hard for anyone who wanted to dance.

The roly-poly man made everyone laugh when he tried to dance with the rag doll. He rolled about so much that he knocked everyone off the floor.

They were all having such a good time. Then suddenly they noticed that all the candles on the Christmas tree were alight!

"Oh, oh! It's time for the Christmas tree!" cried the toys, and they rushed over to it. "Isn't it pretty? Look at the star at the top!"

"Where's the clockwork sailor?" said the roly-poly man.

"Gone to fetch Father Christmas, he told me," said the rocking-horse. "Do you suppose he meant it?"

And then, will you believe it, there came the noise of bells!

"Sleigh bells! It really is Father Christmas coming!" cried all the toys, and they rushed to the chimney. "He's coming! He's coming!"

Down the chimney came a pair of legs – then a pair of red trousers – and then with a jump, down on the rug came a merry, white-whiskered fellow, whose red hood framed his jolly red face.

"Father Christmas! You've come, you've come!" shouted the toys, and they dragged him to the tree.

"Wait a bit – I want my sack. It's just a little way up the chimney," said Father Christmas. So the big teddy bear fetched it. It was a nice big bumpy-looking sack.

"Happy Christmas, toys," said Father Christmas. He was a very nice *little* Father Christmas, not much bigger than the dolls. The toys were glad. They would have been rather afraid of a great big one.

"Happy Christmas!" sang out everyone. Then Father Christmas undid his bag. Oh, what a lot of things he had! There were ribbons and brooches for the dolls, sweets for the soldiers, chocolates for the Noah's Ark animals, and balls, made of red holly berries, for the toy animals. Nobody had been forgotten. It was wonderful.

Father Christmas handed out all the presents, beaming happily. Then he took a few presents from under the tree.

"These are special presents for the people who tried to make your Christmas so nice," he said. "Presents for the golden-haired doll and the twin dolls – and for the black monkey and the pink cat – here you are, special little presents for being kind and good."

"But what about the clockwork sailor?" said the rocking-horse, at once. "He did the tree, you know. Have you forgotten him?"

"Where is he?" said Father Christmas.

Well, dear me, he wasn't there! Would you believe it?

"I saw him last," said the rocking-horse. "He said he was going to fetch you, Father Christmas. *Didn't* he fetch you?"

"Well, I'm here, aren't I?" said Father Christmas, and he laughed. "Dear me – it's sad there's no present for the clockwork sailor, but I don't expect he'll mind at all."

The toys had opened all their presents. Somewhere a clock struck twelve. Midnight! Dear dear, how dreadfully late!

The twin dolls yawned loudly, and that made everyone yawn, too.

"We'd better clear up and go to bed," said the golden-haired doll. "Or we shall fall asleep on our feet, and that would never do."

So they cleared up, and in the middle of it all Father Christmas disappeared. Nobody saw him go. The pink cat said she saw him go into the dolls' house, but he wasn't there when she looked.

Somebody else was, though – the clockwork sailor! The pink cat dragged him out.

"Here's the sailor!" she cried. "Here he is! Sailor, you missed Father Christmas – oh what a terrible pity!"

But, you know, he didn't! He was there all the time. Have you guessed? He was Father Christmas, of course, all dressed up. He had climbed up the chimney when nobody was looking. Wasn't he clever?

"You were Father Christmas!" cried the golden-haired doll, and she hugged him hard. "You're a dear!"

"Yes, you are," shouted the rocking-horse. "That was the best part of all, when Father Christmas came. We were so sad there was no present for you. But you shall have one – you shall, you shall!"

And he did. The toys threaded a whole lot of red holly berries together, and made him the finest necklace he had ever had. Look at him wearing it. Doesn't he look pleased?

Miss Roundy will never guess all that the toys did in her toy-shop that Christmas Day, will she? If you ever meet her, you can tell her. I do wish I'd been there to see it all, don't you?